This igloo book belongs to:

....

igloobooks

Published in 2022
First published in the UK by Igloo Books Ltd
An imprint of Igloo Books Ltd
Cottage Farm, NN6 0BJ, UK
Owned by Bonnier Books
Sveavägen 56, Stockholm, Sweden
www.igloobooks.com

Written by Melanie Joyce
Illustrated by Mikki Butterley

Designed by Stephanie Drake
Edited by Stephanie Moss

0522 001
2 4 6 8 10 9 7 5 3 1
ISBN 978-1-80022-670-8

Printed and manufactured in China

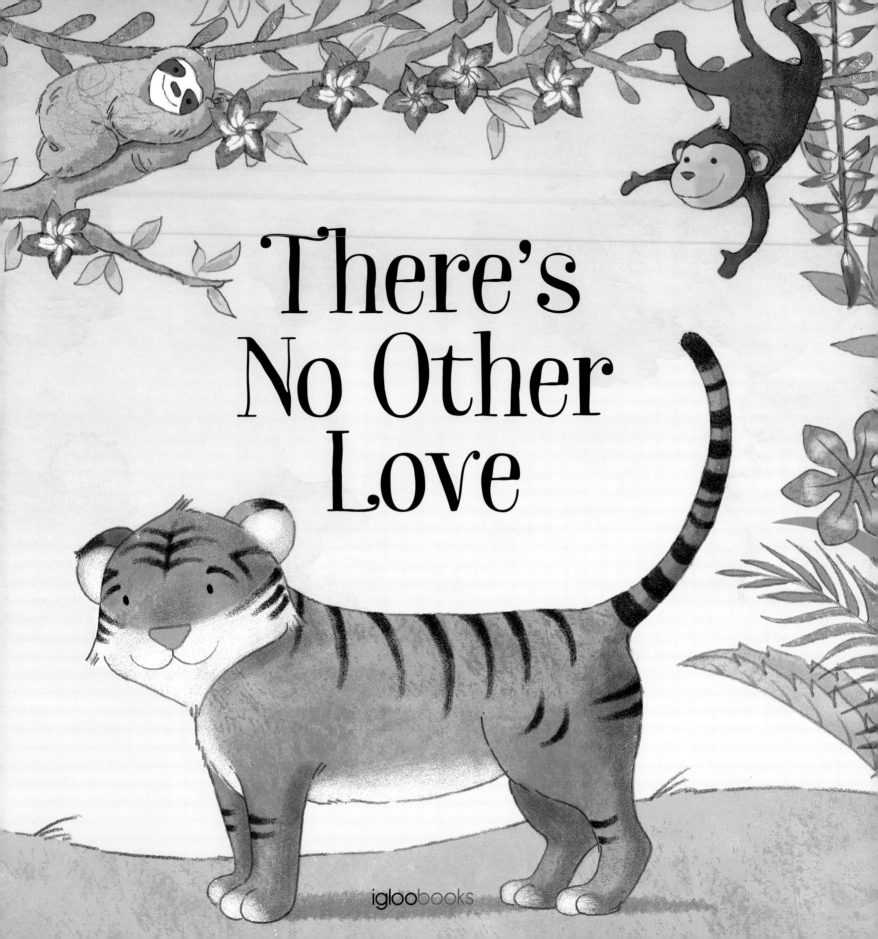

There's No Other Love

igloobooks

There's no other love
like the one I have for you.

Because wherever you go,
I go there, too.

I'll always be there
and I'll never make a fuss.

Nothing and no one
can come between us.

My love is like sunshine on a warm summer's day.

You'll see it in my smile and the fun games we play.

You don't need to worry,
because I'll be by your side...

... on those days when you just
want to run away and hide.

My love is forever and you know it's for real.

There's no need to doubt the way that I feel.

When life gets you down and you feel a bit low,
I'll cheer you up like a pretty rainbow.

My love has no limits, it's as big as the sky
and as gentle as blossom floating down from up high.

Whenever you are lost
and you feel all alone...

... my love will find you
and bring you back home.

If you are scared by the shadows of night...

... my love will be like a soft, guiding light.

There's no other love like yours and mine together.

Our love will never end.
It will go on forever.